ATTITUDE ADJUSTMENT NEEDED NOW!!!

A Workbook For Children With Anger Problems

By

David E. Miller, Ph.D., FICPP
Psychologist

Illustrated By Jennifer Perkins

Attitude Adjustment Needed Now!!!
by David E. Miller, Ph.D., FICPP

Printed in the United States of America

ISBN 1-59781-413-X

www.xulonpress.com

Dedication

    This book is dedicated to several people who have played significant roles in motivating and encouraging me to write it. Among them are the many child patients with anger problems who I have treated in my practice over the past several years. These children and especially their parents struggle to find answers to better management of the inappropriate expression of anger. Temper tantrums and impulsively acting out this emotion is both distressing and embarrassing to parents. Such behaviors often alienate children from peers and result in feelings of rejection and poor self-esteem. Their struggles and sincere search for answers is a daily phenomenon in their lives. My wife, Joy, who consistently upholds me and my patients in prayer; her constant encouragement and support of my ministry to hurting people, provides motivation and stamina for this work. My children, Scott and his wife, Cara, & Lori and her husband, Adam, who frequently express their encouragement and admiration for their dad's work. My grandchildren, Kate, Anna, and Camden who are developing little people; they will need tools for expressing this emotional response appropriately as they learn that life isn't always fair and at times strong emotional responses will naturally result from disappointments, hurts, and the aggressive acts of others. Many thanks are due my godly parents, Rev. L.B. and Ruth Miller, who have encouraged me in my practice and supported it as a ministry to God's people. Their teaching and parenting of me during my growing up years provided an excellent foundation for many of the principles that characterize my approach in helping people in my practice. Finally, this book is dedicated to future generations of children and their families who will search for answers to the symptoms they experience as a result of misunderstanding or inappropriately expressing this emotion.

Table of Contents

Anger..........

Anger is an emotion. Yes, it is a feeling—just like the other feelings I have such as when I feel happy, scared, joyful, excited, or even unsure of myself.

Why do I have such feelings? My doctor told me that all feelings usually happen because something else happens in our life. Like when I got my new puppy—that made me really, really happy. I got excited since I had a new friend to play with. A real puppy that likes to cuddle with you and follows you around is a lot better than pretend playmates or even dolls, teddy bears, or other stuffed animals that I have collected.

Let's learn more about this feeling called ANGER!

Is being angry wrong? NO Absolutely NOT! My doctor told me to always remember that anger is a feeling—the way you express anger makes it look wrong or right.

He said that some people express anger in such a terrible way that it is very wrong to show it in those ways—it hurts other people, may embarrass themselves and their families, and usually doesn't solve anything. It only leads to more problems since they usually get into more trouble.

Other people have learned ways that are okay and they express it without it looking bad or hurting other people. My doctor says that anger usually has a cause and most of the time, being angry at this cause is an OKAY thing! The TRICK is to learn how to express it in an OKAY way—you know what teachers and parents say is APPROPRIATE. "APPROPRIATE" is a big word—but it just means OKAY! My doctor told me that if I show my anger in an APPROPRIATE way, I won't get punished or disciplined...I won't make things worse...and I won't lose privileges that I want to keep. Boy could I use that...I get into a lot of trouble over my anger...both at school and at home. Sometimes my anger even causes my friends to go home when they are at my house playing. Then I get to feeling quite bad and sometimes even say that I HATE MYSELF!

Of course, I don't really mean that but I get so frustrated with myself and what my anger does to my friends and me, that I just don't know what to do. I really need to learn some better ways of dealing with my frustrations.

I told my doctor that the learning tricks idea sounded pretty good to me. I then asked him, "What are these tricks...can I learn them?" He asked me if I had a pet dog and he was glad when I told him I did. He said that dogs are a good thing for kids to have since they teach kids so many things about learning tricks. My dog's name is "Fluffy" since she is so soft and fluffy. He then asked me if she had learned any tricks like sitting down, shaking hands, or chasing a ball. I was proud to tell him she had learned all those tricks and more. You see, I am very proud of my dog—Fluffy and me are great pals!

My doctor told me that if my dog who isn't quite as smart as me can learn these tricks, there was no reason why I couldn't also learn some tricks that might help me with handling my anger. I have to say, I really like this doctor—he always seems to make me feel like I can do things that I didn't feel I could do. He said that he was sure that to teach Fluffy the tricks that she learned, I helped her PRACTICE them. I probably had repeated and repeated the trick until she got it. That was exactly how it happened. Boy my doctor not only knows a lot about kids...he also knows a lot about dogs!

My doctor said that he would teach me 10 tricks that I could start practicing and continue practicing until I had them down pat!

The first trick is for me to just RECOGNIZE that I was getting angry and to tell myself that I am getting angry! I guess most people who get angry have not recognized it until they explode or show their anger in a not so good way—you know the way that usually gets you into further trouble and gets some form of punishment or discipline.

My doctor said that if a friend at school or my little sister was bugging me, I should stop and tell myself right then and there, "This is making me angry!" I'm not sure why it is, but my doctor said that when you just do this—it seems to give you more control over your anger. I guess it has something to do with the trick itself. So, I guess the thing for me to do is to start trying this...I will also ask my parents to help remind me at first since my way of reacting might have become such a habit that it might not be so easy to break it and replace it with this new trick. I will consider my parents' reminding me as a CUE which should help me remember.

When I remember or get the CUE from my parents, I can still choose to make a good decision and either:

1. kindly ask the person to stop doing what they are doing since it is making me angry
2. get away from the person making me angry—go to another place in the room or playground
3. choose to IGNORE this person—just act like I don't even hear what they are saying or see what they are doing
4. inform the teacher or parent of the potential problem this person is trying to cause and ask for

assistance in solving the problem

The main thing here is that I AM STILL IN CONTROL....I have not done anything wrong!

AND I WOULD LIKE TO KEEP IT THAT WAY—IT WILL BE A LOT BETTER IN THE LONG RUN!

The second trick my doctor told me about was what he called **LIG**. I have to confess, I said, "You got to be kidding me doc! What on earth do you mean by LIG?" He explained that LIG simply means **LETTING IT GO!** I asked him if this was kind of like just ignoring something and he agreed! He said that people can learn how to ignore things that previously bugged them—they are in fact choosing to not think about the things that bug them. He said that if you first **RECOGNIZE** that you are getting angry, a second step is to tell yourself that you are going to **LET IT GO** rather than do something about it.

He also said that it is easier to **LIG** something if you get your mind onto something else. He suggested you begin doing something or thinking about something else that you enjoy. I guess it is kind of hard to think about more than one thing at a time, especially if what you choose to think about or do is fun and rewarding. Maybe I should make a list of things I can think about or do during those times I need to **LIG**. You know, have my own grocery list of fun things:

1. playing with Fluffy
2. planning a fun family activity for the weekend

3. spending time helping my dad in the garage work on the car
4. going shopping with my mom
5. going out for ice cream with my family

I'm going to begin constructing my own list of fun things that will help me **LIG** when I need to:

1.
2.
3.
4.
5.
6.
7.
8.
9.
10.

The third trick my doctor told me about was what he called

DEBRIEFING SESSION.

He said that lots of people feel better when they come in and just talk with him. I agree. Just talking about my problem with anger has helped me feel better about it. My doctor told me I could design a form with my teacher or parents that I could use during these times of talking about a situation that might cause me to feel angry. He said it would be important to remember that I might have to hold my anger until I got home or until it was the right time to debrief with someone. But just knowing I can debrief the thing that made me angry seems to help me feel this would be a good thing!

My doctor showed me a DEBRIEFING QUESTIONNAIRE that one of his other patients showed him. It looked pretty easy! Look at the next page to see a sample Debriefing Questionnaire.

Hey I think this thing might just have some potential to help me and other kids having trouble learn how to express their anger.

Debrief Questionnaire

(Check the items that apply. Use comments at bottom to explain.)

___ Someone is getting me upset. Who?
___ I had a bad morning at home.
___ I don't feel well. Should I see the nurse?
___ I just got on punishment at home.
___ I got in trouble on the bus ride to school.
___ I got in trouble in the lunch line.
___ People are distracting or annoying me.
___ People are talking too loud. Who? _
___ I'm mad at someone. Who?
___ People are talking about me. Who?
___ Something is not fair. What?

WHAT WILL MAKE IT BETTER? (check one)

___ Talk to my teacher or parent--debrief
___ Get a drink
___ Ask to take a brief time out
___ Ask to do my work in a different area
___ Hold onto my anger and debrief tonight
___ LIG my anger

___ _____
___ _____

The fourth trick my doctor told me about is what he called COOL OUT. This trick is sort of like TIME OUT except rather than your teacher or parent giving you TIME OUT, you choose it before they have to tell you to do it. My doctor said that if you recognize you are getting angry and that if you stay in the situation further, you might lose control of your anger, you should EXIT the area and get to a more calm place, where you can CALM DOWN and GET YOUR MIND TO FOCUS ON OTHER THINGS. Of course it is important that you get permission to leave the area from the person in charge. If you are at school, you should ask the teacher if you can go to another area of the classroom, the office, the school nurse, or another classroom to cool off. Some teachers and schools allow a student to just take a few minutes in the hall outside the classroom for this cool down time.

If at home, you and your parents may be able to work out a plan so you know at such times you are permitted to go to your room or a play area in the basement or another area of the house. If you just leave and not have permission, that would probably get you into further trouble, and that could be as bad and have the same punishments as if you just let your anger go without any control. So be sure to get this PLAN worked out before you start practicing it. You could even tell your parents or teachers that you are trying to learn better ways to control your anger and you had thought that a COOL DOWN TIME might help you during those times of potential problems.

I think that my parents will really be proud of me if I start coming up with some possible solutions to my anger problems and they will work with me on some of these suggestions.

The fifth trick my doctor shared was something that I have always wanted anyway. Now I have a good reason to ask my parents to help me purchase it and install it in an appropriate place in our basement or garage. This trick involves having a **PUNCHING BAG**. My doctor said that I would need a way to get rid of built up energy on a regular basis. Although physical exercise is good and I should try to do it everyday, he thought that if I felt I was getting mad or felt my anger was beginning to build, I should go to my punching bag and **VENT** these strong feelings on the bag since I couldn't really hurt the bag.

My doctor even shared with me a little about himself and his experience with this trick.

He told me that He got one of these punching bags for his own son when he was younger. Then he even admitted that his son wasn't the only one who used it. He told me that he, himself—my doctor, even found it helpful on some days. So what do you think about that? I'll tell my dad that I'd certainly share my punching bag with him as well—maybe that will help convince him I need it.

My doctor said my parents would really get to appreciate my using the punching bag trick since the walls I use to hit cost a lot of money to repair. Of course, I also know that I would really get into a lot of trouble if I hit my sister when she deserved it. Little sisters or brothers can be nice at times, but I have never known any to not cause their brothers some problems at other times. I think that might be why guys like me have little sisters—just to give them practice in learning to control their anger! I can tell you the truth, if my little sister thinks this is her job, she sure does it well.

But I guess I should thank her since she gives me so many times to practice my new tricks.

The sixth trick my doctor shared is not a new one at all. I have been hearing about this thing from my parents ever since I was born, I think! He said that boys and girls could eliminate some things that make them angry by simply doing what's expected and following the rules. For example, when I follow the rules mom and dad give me and do my chores without being reminded, things seem to be okay. It's when I forget to do a chore that is assigned or ignore a rule that I know has to be followed that they either complain to me or yell at me. I don't like being yelled at or complained to and I have to admit that in the past, I would get angry at these times.

My doctor said that this sixth trick would certainly take care of this problem and I would have no reason to get angry—since no one would "BE ON MY BACK." This trick is what my doctor referred to as FCR. Now I have to admit to you, I ask him what in the world could FCR stand for? He quickly responded to my question. He said FCR stands for FIRST CALL RESPONSE. Yes, you guessed it! FCR simply means that if my parents or teacher would ask me to do something, I do it right then and do not require a reminder. I guess I have been guilty in the past of requiring second, third, fourth, and sometimes fifth call reminders. It is sort of funny, but my parents' frustration levels seem to get higher with each reminder. By the time they are at number 4 or 5, I know I can expect some type of consequence. I usually get a discipline in addition to several minutes of lecture about the importance of following directions, obeying the rules, listening to teachers and parents, etc. etc. etc. You probably got my point by now...it is far better to just do it on the **FIRST CALL**, then you can avoid all this follow-up stuff that you, like me, will find quite boring and might even make you angry.

I sometimes think my parents get angry when I require so many reminders, but they might also just be somewhat disappointed in me. I think they want me to show that I am growing up and will turn our okay! I think they just want to be proud of me. When I act responsible and obey the rules and meet up to their expectations without needing several reminders, I can tell they are very happy. I LIKE FOR MY PARENTS TO BE HAPPY WITH ME—IT IS A MUCH BETTER LIFE!

I think I will set a goal for myself: my goal will be to never require more than one reminder. Maybe I can even remember to do my chores without any reminders! That would be SUPER!

F IRST

C ALL

R ESPONSE

The seventh trick my doctor introduced to me was what he called the BIG C Plan. He waited for me to ask what this plan was, but I thought I had a pretty good idea since I figured that the "C" had to stand for something pretty important. After thinking about it briefly, I asked him if this trick had anything to do with COOPERATION. He was so pleased that I had figured it out on my own. I confessed to him that my parents seem to remind me of the importance of COOPERATION almost daily. They tell me that cooperation is so important in everything I do—at school, on the playground, in my back yard, with my sister, and with them.

My doctor said that this "C" word is perhaps one of the most important things a kid can remember. It is most important to COOPERATE which shows others you have a good attitude. I guess that kids who have anger problems and showing that they need an ATTITUDE ADJUSTMENT also have problems with cooperation. My doctor said that if you work on changing your attitude, you will also show more cooperation. If you work on becoming more cooperative, your attitude begins to adjust. It doesn't matter which one you work on first—work on either one, and the other one improves as well.

WHAT A DEAL...that's just like a blue light special at WALMART! Two for the price of one...or something like that.

All righty then...I'm going to start showing more cooperation starting right now! Yes, it will take a lot of effort, but I also plan on becoming more cooperative with my little sister. She will be a very large challenge...but I can do it! I'm learning lots of tricks to help me with the improved ATTITUDE.

The eighth trick my doctor shared with me is one that he said works with anger just like it works with other problems that kids sometimes have like ADD or ADHD. He called this trick the

STOP...THINK...DO... PROGRAM.

This program is a little more involved than the first few tricks but it is still pretty simple. It goes like this.....

GOOD DECISIONS ARE MADE IN 3 SIMPLE STEPS:

1—STOP

2—THINK

3—DO

It's kind of like a traffic light. You remember what we learned in preschool and kindergarten classes:

RED means STOP
YELLOW means SLOW DOWN
GREEN means GO

Now if you can think about the traffic light idea...

Red will mean STOP
Yellow will mean THINK
&
Green will mean DO

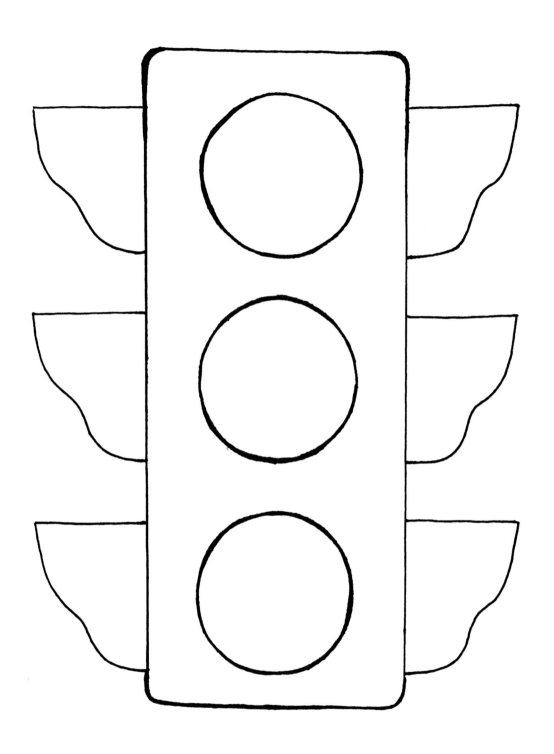

Color the 1st light red which will stand for **STOP...**

Color the 2nd light yellow which will stand for THINK...

Color the 2nd light yellow which will stand for **THINK...**

Color the 3rd light green which will stand for

DO . . .

Now let's get this idea into our computer (you know—your brain)

Let's say:

STOP...THINK...DO...

Let's say it again:

STOP...THINK...DO...

Now let's say it 5 times as fast as we can!

My doctor said that his patients with ADD or ADHD use this Stop...Think...Do...Program for helping them make good decisions. He said when you make a decision before you stop and think about possible solutions, you are making an IMPULSIVE decision. He made it sound like IMPULSIVE DECISIONS are not good ones. He also said that most people who make impulsive decisions usually regret it later since they realize that it wasn't the best decision. He said it is important for people to think about the possible answers to problems rather than just quickly choose the first thing that comes to their minds.

My doctor is a pretty cool guy—he told me that he used the STOP...THINK...DO...Program himself! He even told me that when he got in a hurry and didn't stop to think about his options prior to deciding, that many times he had to go back and correct a bad decision since it was one of those IMPULSIVE ones. To hear him talk about this makes it sound pretty important. I'm going to learn this STOP...THINK...Do...thing if it can help me stay out of trouble! I'll do anything to stay out of trouble...it is worth the effort and work to do it!

My doctor had another great idea to help me remember the stop...think...do...program. We made stickers at one of our appointments on his computer. Now I put these stickers on my notebook, homework assignment sheet, and book bag. We also made little cards that stand up and put stickers on them so my parents could place them throughout the house at important places like my dresser, night stand, in front of my cereal bowl at breakfast, and you guessed it, even in the bathroom in the morning so I can be reminded even while I'm brushing my teeth. The more reminders I have, the easier it is for me to remember.

I showed one of my cards to my teacher and asked her if I could display one on my desk—just to remind me to stop and think before I acted. I told her it was a plan that my doctor, parents, and me all worked out to help me learn better control of my anger. She really like the idea! She said it would be okay to place one on top of my desk to help me remember to stop and think before I made my decision. She also really made me feel important when she asked me to talk with my doctor about making a few extra stickers and card signs for other students in the classroom who might want one on their desk as well. I guess I am not the only person who has trouble with anger or making good decisions.

My doctor was very pleased with this request. We made several stickers and cards in my next appointment. I felt pretty important when I brought these in to my teacher.

It sure feels a lot better—and I do mean a lot—to be on the good side of your teacher rather than in trouble so much!

Now my parents have begun to be quite proud of me for being a good student and helping myself and my peers with problems rather than causing them!

> **I AM IN CONTROL NOW!**
> **JUST STOP...**
> **THINK...THEN DO!**
> **CONTROL IS THE WORD!**

Here are two examples of the stickers we made in my last session:

> **MANAGE ANGER BY:**
> **STOPPING**
> **THINKING**
> **then... DOING**

My doctor and me also made a poster for my room. Yes, you guessed it...another reminder to stop...think...before I choose to do!

I'd really like to find a flashing traffic light for my room at home. Maybe my teacher might also want one for our classroom. That would really be a cool way to help all of us students who have anger problems to learn how to better manage this emotion. I'm going to look for one of these special lamps the next time we are shopping at the department store. My doctor said he got his at the local K-mart store. I will probably check there first!

Here is an example of the poster we made for my room... (you can color in the arrows if you like)

STOP
STOP
STOP

Think...Think... & Think !

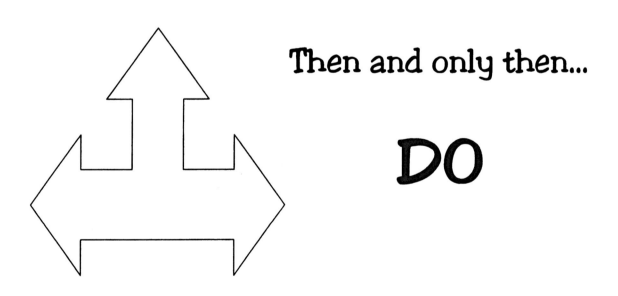

Then and only then...

DO

I asked my mom and dad to get some sticker forms at the office store so we could make our own stickers on the computer. They said, "Sure...we really like this stop...think...do...program; it is really helping you learn how to control your anger." I said, "That makes three of us...I am glad I'm learning to make better decisions on how to deal with the day to day problems that kids have."

And so...I think my doctor said he had 10 tricks in all, and we have covered just 8. Let's talk about the last 2 tricks.

The ninth trick my doctor told me about was what he called **THE REWARD SYSTEM.** He said that most kids are just like me; they like rewards, gifts, tokens, charts, certificates, etc. etc. etc... He explained that a kid can kind of design the REWARD SYSTEM with his or her parents—a system that is designed especially for that specific kid! He said that most parents will know what their child really enjoys doing; and so they set up the system to provide a means to earn EXTRA time doing that activity. For example, I enjoy playing computer games, but my parents limit me to only 30 minutes per day. If I control my anger and avoid temper tantrums, I can earn an extra 15 minutes per day.

Now that really helps me remember to CONTROL myself even when something happens that makes me angry. Sometimes my parents remind me with a CUE that we have worked out between us. The CUE serves as a warning and "reminder" to make a choice that keeps me from spoiling the reward I am working on.

My parents said they would help me remember at first by using the CUE, but expected me to improve to a level that I could remember on my own without the need for their CUE.

Some of my friends have similar reward systems that include charts with check marks, happy or sad faces, stars, or some other marking that lets them know how they are doing in earning the extra privilege or reward. Other systems that I have heard about involve the kid getting TOKENS that are then cashed in for the reward. I guess it doesn't really matter what system is designed for you as long as it works to help you gain more control over your anger.

THE REWARD SYSTEM

The tenth and last trick my doctor shared with me is what he called **TALK SYSTEMS**. I guess it is also called a big word—MEDIATION THERAPY and some psychologists call it a LIFE SPACE INTERVIEW. But this is really no more than talking about the problem by answering 4 questions. It is kind of like DEBRIEFING that we learned about earlier. The 4 questions that need answered when a kid is trying to understand his anger and solve the problem are as follows:

1. What did you do wrong? (Identifying the problem)
2. What happens when you do this? (Consequence)

3. What should you have done rather than what you did? (Alternative solutions)
4. Will you promise to do this alternative the next time this problem occurs? (Commitment to change)

These questions will probably be asked by your parent, teacher, or other adult in charge of you; and, when you answer them, it should help you learn to think through such problems logically. Sometimes, the adult might also have you PRACTICE the alternative by role playing the situation again—you know a "make believe situation" that the adult describes and then asks you how you would respond. If you choose the right response, then that's usually the end of it since they know you learned from this talking process. If you choose the wrong answer, though, you might need to prepare yourself for some additional role plays. My doctor told me that if a kid cooperates with this system and has a good attitude, usually the whole thing only takes about 5 to 10 minutes. However, if a BAD ATTITUDE enters into the picture and COOPERATION becomes a problem, the system may take longer and decrease the time available for other more exciting activities and playtime.

So there you have it...10 tricks to help you manage anger better! Again, let's be sure to remember that anger itself is not bad...it is how you choose to express it that makes it bad or unacceptable!

Perhaps if I review the 10 tricks again by drawing my own pictures or making charts on the following pages, I will remember them better.

Here is a picture to help me just remember my first trick, which is **RECOGNIZE** that I am angry. I might benefit from CUES given to me by my parents or teacher.

This drawing helps me to think about **LIG** or **LIGGING** my problem.

This third picture will remind me of a great trick—the
DEBRIEFING SESSION.

My fourth trick—The COOL
OUT—would look like this:

If the first four tricks aren't helpful, I can always try number 5—THE PUNCHING BAG PROGRAM.

My sixth option is no other than **FCR (First Call Response)** which helps to PREVENT anger from forming inside me.

The **BIG C PLAN** works to help with many problems kids face; it is a great option for helping to deal with anger. This drawing reminds me of this option.

Another important trick for solving many problems I might have is the STOP...THINK...DO... Program. I like this one since it helps me to avoid being IMPULSIVE! You can make stickers or posters to remind you to practice it.

The ninth trick involves
REWARD SYSTEMS–
tokens, check marks, happy faces, extra privileges, etc. This picture can remind me of this option:

My tenth and last trick is **TALK SYSTEMS**—it might look like the following picture:

PARENT'S SECTION OF MY BOOK

Characteristics of Anger or Conduct Problems With Children
(as specified in Diagnostic and Statistical Manual of Mental Disorders, Fourth Edition, Text Revision, published by American Psychiatric Association, Washington, DC, 2000)

CONDUCT DISORDER

A repetitive and persistent pattern of behavior in which the basic rights of others or major age-appropriate societal norms or rules are violated, as manifested by the presence of three (or more) of the following criteria in the past 12 months, with at least one criterion present in the past 6 months:

Aggression to people and animals
(1) often bullies, threatens, or intimidates others
(2) often initiates physical fights
(3) has used a weapon that can cause serious physical harm to others (e.g., a bat, brick, broken bottle, knife, gun)
(4) has been physically cruel to people
(5) has been physically cruel to animals
(6) has stolen while confronting a victim (e.g., mugging, purse snatching, extortion, armed robbery)
(7) has forced someone into sexual activity

Destruction of property
(8) has deliberately engaged in fire setting with the intention of causing serious damage
(9) has deliberately destroyed others' property (other than by fire setting)

Deceitfulness or theft
(10) has broken into someone else's house, building, or car
(11) lies to obtain goods or favors or to avoid obligations (i.e., "cons" others)
(12) has stolen items of nontrivial value without confronting a victim (e.g., shoplifting, but without breaking and entering; forgery)

Serious violations of rules
(13) often stays out at night despite parental prohibitions, beginning before age 13 years
(14) has run away from home overnight at least twice while living in parental or parental surrogate home (or once without returning for a lengthy period)
(15) is often truant from school, beginning before age 13 years

Diagnostic Codes Used By Your Doctor:

312.81 Conduct Disorder, Childhood-Onset Type *(onset of at least one criterion characteristic of Conduct Disorder prior to age 10 years)*

312.82 Conduct Disorder, Adolescent-Onset Type *(absence of any criteria characteristic of Conduct Disorder prior to age 10 years)*

312.89 Conduct Disorder, Unspecified Onset *(age at onset is not known)*

Oppositional Defiant Disorder

A pattern of negativistic, hostile, and defiant behavior lasting at least 6 months, during which four (or more) of the following are present:

(1) often loses temper
(2) often argues with adults
(3) often actively defies or refuses to comply with adults' requests or rules
(4) often deliberately annoys people
(5) often blames others for his or her mistakes or misbehavior
(6) is often touchy or easily annoyed by others
(7) is often angry and resentful
(8) is often spiteful or vindictive

Diagnostic Codes Used By Your Doctor:

313.81 Oppositional Defiant Disorder
312.9   Disruptive Behavior Disorder Not Otherwise Specified

Adjustment Disorders

The development of emotional or behavioral symptoms in response to an identifiable stressor(s) occurring within 3 months of the onset of the stressor(s) and symptoms or behaviors which are clinically significant as evidenced by either of the following:

(1) marked distress that is in excess of what would be expected from exposure to the stressor
(2) significant impairment in social or occupational (academic) functioning

The stress-related disturbance:

- (3) does not meet the criteria for another disorder and is not merely an exacerbation of a preexisting disorder
- (4) does not represent Bereavement
- (5) once the stressor (or its consequences) has terminated, the symptoms do not persist for more than 6 months

Diagnostic Codes Used By Your Doctor:

309.0 Adjustment Disorder With Depressed Mood *(when the predominant manifestations are symptoms such as depressed mood, tearfulness, or feelings of hopelessness)*

309.24 Adjustment Disorder With Anxiety *(when the predominant manifestations are symptoms such as nervousness, worry, or jitteriness, or, in children, fears of separation from major attachment figures)*

309.28 Adjustment Disorder With Anxiety and Depressed Mood *(when the predominant manifestation is a combination of depression and anxiety)*

309.3 Adjustment Disorder With Disturbance of Conduct *(when the predominant manifestation is a disturbance in conduct in which there is violation of the rights of others or of major age-appropriate societal norms and rules (e.g., truancy, vandalism, reckless driving, fighting, defaulting on legal responsibilities)*

309.4 Adjustment Disorder With Mixed Disturbance of Emotions and Conduct *(when the predominant manifestations are both emotional symptoms (e.g., depression, anxiety) and a disturbance of conduct*

309.9 Adjustment Disorder—Unspecified *(for maladaptive reactions (e.g., physical complaints, social withdrawal, or work or academic inhibition) to stressors that are not classifiable as one of the specific subtypes of Adjustment Disorder*

Treatment of Children Experiencing Anger Problems

Generally, the treatment for children experiencing problems with anger must involve several steps in process:

(1) Evaluation to thoroughly diagnose this condition and rule out other factors that may appear to manifest the same symptoms
(2) Environmental alterations to reduce level of stimulae and to significantly increase the level of structure within the child's environment
(3) Assess and insure that expectations on child by parental and authority figures is age appropriate and consistent between care givers
(4) Cognitive-Behavioral therapy to help child develop and learn coping strategies that will enable better management of anger and impulsive features
(5) Cognitive-Behavioral therapy to help child learn that experiencing anger is not necessarily wrong, but an emotional response to something occurring in his/her life; and, that inappropriate expression of anger makes it wrong
(6) Cognitive-Behavioral therapy to help child learn appropriate ways to vent anger productively and eliminate non-productive and unacceptable expressions
(7) Evaluation of symptoms to determine if medication might be helpful in management of impulsive symptoms during therapy with child

Medication is usually not an initial step in treating children with anger problems, but, one that might be considered later in the process. To only medicate a child who is exhibiting symptoms of impulsive acting out his/her anger will not help in the constructive learning of coping skills and alternative behaviors. Both behavioral therapy and environmental interventions, including an increase in structure for the child, will be absolutely necessary even if medication is indicated.

When medication is indicated as part of the treatment approach for a child, extreme care is given in the selection of appropriate medications and then monitored very closely by the child's pediatrician or family physician. Fortunately, over the years, physicians and pediatricians have learned better ways to prescribe the medications and have slowed the whole process down. Rather than starting a child on the therapeutic dosage as recommended by the PDR according to the child's age and weight, the new approach to starting medication is very different. Generally, the beginning dosages of such medications are only ½ the therapeutic dosage or a very small dosage—which we know is not going to be effective in controlling the symptoms.

We start the medication at this ineffective dosage for the first few days so that the child's body can get use to the medication. After the first few days (5 to 7 days), the medication dosage is moved upward. We call this "titration" which means a gradual increase of the medication to what the appropriate dosage should be. By slowing down the introduction of the medication to the body, we can certainly reduce the side effects the child experiences and many times eliminate possible side effects all together. We have learned that side effects of many medications are usually dosage related.

Before discarding the possibility of medication due to possible side effects, you should be reminded that to not give a child medication that he/she really needs to increase successfully managing his/her behaviors is just as wrong as over medicating the child with unnecessary medications or the wrong dosage of medication. Perhaps you should look up the possible side effects of the common drugs that most of us wouldn't think twice prior to taking—Aspirin, Tylenol or Ibprofen. You will discover that even these drugs have a fairly long list of possible side effects and could be dangerous—perhaps even more dangerous than the medications recommended in your son or daughter's treatment. Please remember that just because the drug manufacturers and PDR list possible side effects to the medications, the majority of people taking medications do not experience these side effects. All medications should be monitored closely by your child's physician and administered precisely as prescribed to reduce possible side effects.

Common side effects of psycho-stimulant medications include the following:

- Loss of appetite
- Insomnia or trouble sleeping
- Sleepiness or over sedation
- Emotional upset or sadness
- Depression
- Fearfulness
- Social withdrawal
- Headaches
- Nail biting
- Stomach upset
- Weight loss

- Irritability
- Behavior rebound when medication is used up

Common side effects of SSRI medications include the following:

- Dry mouth
- Nausea
- Headache
- Diarrhea
- Insomnia
- Sleepiness or over sedation
- Nervousness
- Tiredness
- Constipation
- Sweating
- Abdominal pain
- Sexual response problems

The influence of environmental factors appears to be very significant—especially in reinforcing or worsening the behaviors and characteristics of children. Some children have a very difficult time making transitions from one activity to another. If the home environment is characterized by chaos, or a lack of structure and consistency from one day to the next, the child may react with agitation, angry outbursts, temper, or some other form of inappropriate behavior. Most of us operate from a heavily stressed schedule, carrying our day-planners and palm pilot schedulers as well as cell phones with us everywhere we go. Our typical tempo is excessive and we get very impatient if we experience traffic problems or highway construction that delays our arrival at our destination according to our planned arrival time. Children in this culture begin seeing this form of modeling from the adults in their lives quite early and as a result of significant modeling, they begin emulating this same behavior. Some experts in the field refer to this influence as the "hurried society" concept. Children begin responding to inconveniences with the same level of agitation, anger, impatience that they see modeled for them by the "significant" others in their lives.

HELPFUL INTERVENTIONS FOR DEALING WITH MY ANGRY OR OUT OF CONTROL CHILD

Most parents are anxious to learn more about helping their son or daughter who is struggling with the expression of anger. The following is a collection of ideas, gathered from various sources and many years experience, which might prove helpful to parents and teachers working with such children.

1. **Establish a structured environment with a very predictable routine:**

   - All children seem to do better with structure. Children who become frustrated with the routine and expectations constantly changing will often express such emotion through a temper outburst or some other form of anger
   - The more predictable the routine and schedule, the better he/she will manage such changes
   - Transitions from one activity to another can be challenging for many children; routines or schedules that form a consistent pattern seems to decrease the difficulty in making the change in activities
   - When it is necessary to change the routine for some special event or crisis, prepare the child in advance by explaining the anticipated change in schedule and reassuring him/her of how the usual tasks will be handled
   - Verbally preparing the child about an impending change in routine, and giving them time to complete the current activity prior to the transition can reduce the stress such a change poses for the child
   - School nights should have a consistent schedule that is kept with a time for homework, dinner, playtime, recreation or family time, bedtime, etc. that doesn't change from night to night
   - Morning routines should be similar with the same tasks expected each morning in preparation for school
   - A chart or written schedule of the routine will provide an excellent visual aid that can help the child stay on task

2. **Get the child's attention:**
   - While not embarrassing the child by calling special attention to him/her in class or in public, try to develop

and agree on a discreet method with the child ahead of time
- Make frequent contact with the child (pat on the back or shoulder, etc.)
- Use signals such as tapping or snapping fingers
- Vary your tone of voice, speed or delivery, and expression to avoid boredom
- Make frequent eye contact with the child; eye contact during talking to someone is very powerful

3. **Provide encouragement and remain positive**
   - Be sure to reward or reinforce as many behaviors as those that are punished or disciplined; this helps to balance things and can help guard against damaging the child's self-esteem
   - Try to praise immediately any and all positive behaviors or successful performance; discipline for inappropriate behaviors can be delayed for better timing and the ability to process the misbehavior with the child
   - Look for ways to encourage and build up the child struggling with anger as such children typically are struggling with low self-esteem; such children typically get more negative attention through discipline or punishment as compared to positive attention through recognition and compliments
   - Teach the child to begin rewarding him/herself through self-talk ("You did very well remaining calm and not displaying inappropriate anger...doesn't that make you feel more proud?"); this encourages the child to think more positively about him/herself
   - Give the child struggling with anger responsibilities which are within his/her capacity even if the task assigned requires extra help or supervision; acceptance and recognition of efforts should be emphasized by the adult
   - Increase the child's self-esteem by avoiding situations in which he/she is likely to experience repeated failures; ask the child struggling with anger or apt to become frustrated to accomplish things that utilize his/her stronger abilities and hence are likely to be completed successfully; as confidence grows, more challenging tasks can be attempted

4. **Be attentive to and make necessary changes to ENVIRONMENT**

- Set up a separate room or part of a room as his/her special area for play or study; keep the décor simple and uncluttered; arrange a work table or desk facing a blank wall to avoid unnecessary distractions
- Reduce stimulation and possible distractions by turning off radio/TV while performing tasks which require concentration (homework); multiple stimuli interferes with focusing on the primary task
- Limit playmates to one at a time for the angry child; by limiting the stimuli in the environment, he/she can experience more success
- Insure there is sufficient time for physical activity in daily schedule; it is important that children have a means of "venting" pinned up energy
- Avoid over-stimulating or excessive schedules that often result when the child is participating in too many extra curricular activities; encourage participation in one but avoid over-participation
- Seat the angry child near the teacher's desk in the classroom, but include as part of regular classroom seating to avoid stigma or made to feel different than peers
- Surround the angry child with "good role models" preferably other children that he/she views as "significant others;" encourage peer interaction, cooperative collaborative learning between the students
- Avoid boredom but limit over-stimulation in schedule, routines, or atmosphere
- Review goals and expectations of child to ensure they are within age or normal developmental standards

5. **Giving instructions or assigning tasks should be kept simple:**
   - Avoid giving complex or multiple tasks; keep things very simple and easy to understand; instructions should be short and clear
   - Insure that the child understands the direction, task, or request by asking him/her to repeat it to you
   - If necessary, repeat the task for the child in a calm positive manner
   - Simplify or break down complex directions; instructions should be presented one at a time; avoid giving multiple commands
   - The list of rules should not be too long for the child to comprehend

- Posting the list of rules for a visual cue can be helpful
- Help the child feel comfortable in seeking assistance as many children will not ask for additional help or clarification
- Plan to give assistance longer than for normal children; gradually reduce assistance as possible
- Maintain eye contact while giving verbal instruction; encourage the child to listen with his ears, eyes, and body—that helps to improve ability to focus on task
- Be consistent with daily or repetitive activities/instructions
- Demonstrate slowly and carefully any new task or difficult assignment, showing the child the proper actions accompanied by short, clear, quiet, explanations; do not over-load the child's short-term memory; repeat the demonstration as often as necessary and until learned; be patient as the child may take longer than expected to form memory traces
- Do one thing at a time; give the child one toy at a time to play with or assign one task at a time for him/her to complete

6. Provide appropriate supervision and practice limit setting:

- Place appropriate boundaries or limits on the child to help him/her make good decisions and be successful in their endeavors; the angry child often lacks the ability to think through the consequences of an action prior to deciding to do it
- Remain calm, state the infraction of the rule or misbehavior; don't debate or argue with the child; never argue with the angry child, it will only tend to escalate the frustration of both the child and the adult involved
- While it might be appropriate to administer the consequences immediately, it will often be more effective if you let the child know that consequences will be forthcoming but determined at a later time; sometimes delaying the consequence is effective to deter further misbehavior as the child experiences what we call "therapeutic anxiety" while awaiting action on his/her misbehavior
- Discipline should be focused on learning rather than mere punishment; administer without harshness but remain as neutral and non-reactive as possible

- Avoid any ridicule or criticism; remember the angry child has difficulty staying in control—it is the nature of anger management problems
- Avoid publicly reminding the child of his problem; avoid correcting him in public when possible; discipline should be handled privately most of the time
- Learn to recognize warning signals that can help predict future problems; when they appear, quietly intervene, adjust the task, remove the child from the immediate environment, or redirect the child's focus in order to prevent explosive episodes
- Do not pity, indulge, be frightened by or manipulated by the angry child; the child needs to see your strength not weakness
- Do not give into tantrums; if the angry child knows he/she can get away without complying with a request by throwing a temper tantrum, this will become a common tool to avoid requested tasks; quietly inform him/her that when the protest is done, the task will still be waiting for his attention

7. **Try to enlarge your patience and ability to tolerate the various idiosyncrasies that most children who experience anger problems exhibit:**
   - Accept the fact that the child may not at first be capable of managing his/her anger and the behaviors that accompany it—he/she can learn adaptive behaviors and learn better control of anger with sufficient time, training, and support
   - Don't personalize attacks or feel the need to retaliate when the angry child's behavior is vented toward you—recognize that it is not a personal attack despite how personalized it feels
   - Practice the philosophy: "Problems are Opportunities" as you approach or strategize handling one of many of the challenges that this child will provide both parents and teachers
   - Get support from others in handling the daily frustrations by talking with other parents or teachers; you will discover that as you share frustrations with others, this form of "venting" is therapeutic and seems to enlarge your patience
   - Try to remember that the angry child is a unique person who needs help in learning appropriate expression of this

strong emotion, rather than see him/her as abnormal, a problem, or as having a non-reversible disorder
- Expand your knowledge base regarding this condition through available resources (i.e. books, audio and video tapes, seminars, workshops, etc.)
- Each evening, take a moment to think about the day and to forgive the child for any possible transgressions; acknowledge the anger or resentment, disappointment or other negative emotions that may have arisen throughout the day due to the child's misbehavior; don't allow resentments to affect your love for and relationship with the child
- Be sure to have "special times" with the child for recreation, fun, or relationship building times; such times helps to counter-balance the times of discipline that follow a misbehavior and helps improve the child's self esteem

8. **Some helpful hints for the adults working with angry children:**
   - Avoid falling into the trap of being endlessly negative: "Stop...Don't Do That...No...You are not listening again...You need to settle down...You are not focusing...You are showing your anger again..."
   - Remember that under stress, people tend to regress to previous habits; re-directing the child who has regressed to expressing anger is better than to viciously confront him/her
   - Don't personalize the child's misbehavior or even his/her verbal attacks—it's really not about you so don't take it personally
   - Try hard to keep your emotions under control; try to appear "cool, calm, and collected" by bracing yourself for expected turmoil
   - Keep your voice calm; speak quietly and slowly as this approach can help to de-escalate the child and perhaps prevent the escalation that can end in a crisis or power struggle
   - Avoid using analogies—things must be kept simple and straight forward
   - Don't lecture the angry child; when intervening because of misbehavior or an inappropriate display of anger, keep it simple and brief; anything longer than 5 minutes becomes a "lecture" to the child and he/she will be apt to "turn you off" or discount the content of your discussion

100

- Do not make promises (implied or explicit) that you cannot/do not plan to fulfill
- Look diligently for positive behaviors which you can reinforce; be sincere when praising the child as he/she will quickly discern any lack of sincerity
- Remember to make a distinction between the behavior which you do not like and the child him/herself who you love (i.e. "I love you, but I don't like the way you showed your anger toward your sister...")
- KNOW YOURSELF! Be aware of your own personal "hooks" or those things that might trigger anger or some other emotional response in you

9. Provide a MODEL for appropriate expression of anger

- James Dobson, Ph.D. has said that "more things are caught than taught" in child development; it is important that the adults around children provide a role model of what appropriate expression of anger looks like rather than demand behavior from the child that they do not practice themselves
- Relationship will probably be the most powerful tool an adult has with a child; a good relationship will have a positive influence in enabling both the parent and teacher to suggest alternative behaviors for expression of anger. As the child's relationship increases, he/she will want to please the adult and therefore be open to that adult's suggestions
- Without the foundation of a good relationship with the child, many parents and teachers resort to intimidation, threats, or fear as a means of forcing/imposing their will upon the child
- To create a good relationship with a child, the adult must be seen as:
    1. fair—avoiding favorites, and not over-reacting
    2. honest—always telling the truth, living up to promises made
    3. caring—getting involved with the child's life, sharing self with child, becoming interested in the little things important to the child
    4. right—demonstrating a sense of right vs. wrong
    5. responsible—explaining rules, but being flexible; demonstrating a willingness to compromise when possible
    6. dependable—keeping any promise made

7. respectful of others—mutual trust demonstrated for the other parent, co-workers, teacher, etc. (children can trust you since you trust others and they trust you)

10. **Remember that all behavior—both positive and negative—is valid and has meaning; misbehavior needs to be understood, not necessarily punished**

11. **Sometimes understanding the behavior eliminates the need to intervene or helps to plan appropriate interventions to correct or alter the pattern**

Common Myths That Worry Parents

1. **Anger problems are the result of poor parenting:**
   While poor parenting techniques can worsen or enlarge a child's problem with the expression of anger, it is not always the result of poor parenting. Some children are born with a tendency toward being "strong-willed" and thus will have less tolerance for things not going their way. Such children might also have parents or other significant others in their life that display anger and thus the child's "strong will" nature tends to get reinforced as acceptable since seeing it modeled by others.

2. **Labeling a child with a diagnosis of Conduct Disorder or Oppositional Defiant Disorder is harmful:**
   Labels are tools that help us in organizing and understanding concepts. In the case of properly diagnosing a child, then assigning that label to him/her could facilitate providing that child with the proper treatment and accommodations necessary for success. A diagnosis is far better than labels given to these children by their peers and even some teachers (bad student, obnoxious, lazy, irresponsible, unmotivated, trouble maker, weirdo, crazy, etc.)

3. **Children with anger problems usually always have ADD/ADHD or some other problem as well:**
   While the child experiencing problems with the expression of anger may have other problems such as ADD/ADHD, a problem with anger can and often does stand alone and not caused by the frustration experienced with other problems such as ADD/ADHD. The child may become fairly active during temper tantrums and show excessive energy at other times—usually caused more by anxiety, this "anxious" energy is different than hyperactivity or ADD/ADHD.

4. **Medication should only be a last resort and only given when nothing else works:**
   While medication may be indicated to help reduce depressive or anxiety symptoms of the angry child, it is not always indicated. When a child is exhibiting compensatory behaviors that appear to be symptoms of depression or anxiety, it is often helpful to consider a small dosage of one of the anti-depressant medications. However, medication alone to treat the angry child is never appropriate; other interventions including therapy, parental guidance and support, and

environmental alterations are absolutely necessary even if the child is taking medication to help reduce his/her symptoms. It is most important that the child learn better coping skills and gain understanding of the appropriate expression of this emotion, rather than merely suppressing it.

To avoid giving a child medication when really necessary to treat the problem is neglectful! It would be just as bad to under-medicate as to over-medicate or use medication when it is not needed. Medication helps the child manage symptoms that are neurologically or chemically based while therapy and environmental interventions helps him/her develop coping skills for better managing this emotion.

The child's pediatrician should always be consulted whenever medication is recommended; in fact, coordination of the child's treatment with the pediatrician is highly recommended even when medication isn't part of his/her care.

5. **If I agree to use medication with my child, I can skip the therapy or other treatments suggested to treat his/her problems:**
While medication may help to reduce symptoms, it will be important that the child learn coping skills and better ways to express his anger and other emotional responses. This is the purpose of therapy—to help the child replace previous habits with newly learned methods and coping skills. It is hoped that by applying his/her new learning and coping skills, the medication can be temporary and eventually discontinued. It is important that the physician who prescribed the medication take charge of the discontinuation rather than the parent or child doing this on their own.

6. **The only medication available for treating children with any problem seems to be Ritalin or one of the other drugs like Ritalin:**
While at an earlier time in history, Ritalin (Methylphenidate hydrochloride) was probably the preferred if not the only medication that had been approved and therefore utilized in the treatment of children's hyperactivity and impulsivity, drug companies have continued to work on discovering and developing better medications with significantly fewer side effects than Ritalin. Subsequent to the Ritalin era, Dexedrine, Cylert, and Adderall were developed and utilized by

Pediatricians for the same conditions that Ritalin previously treated. In more recent years, additional medications have been approved for treating children for a variety of symptoms; these include Metadate, Concerta, and Provigil. For several years now, pediatricians have also utilized the anti-depressant medications for the management of many of the same symptoms. Especially with adolescent children, there has been a move toward the SSRI anti-depressant medications (Prozac, Paxil, and Zoloft) due to their safety and ease in monitoring. Perhaps one of the best advantages of utilizing the anti-depressants rather than stimulant medications is that usually dosing is only once per day and the benefits of the medications last longer into the day without the typical "rebound" effect that Ritalin and some of the other stimulant medications have.

7. **Physicians are too prone to prescribe medication without considering side effects and the severity of the child's problem:**
   Most pediatricians and physicians are essentially not willing to prescribe any medications without a thorough evaluation of the child's condition and then will insist that the child see a counselor or psychologist in addition to taking the appropriate medication. When the medication is being prescribed, the physician will want to discuss such things as: (a) the child's age and weight, (b) the severity of the symptoms, (c) the specific target symptoms that will be treated by the medication, (d) whether problems such as learning disabilities, enuresis (bed-wetting), anxiety or depression need to be considered, (e) if a long-acting or short-acting medication would be more effective, (f) how often and when the medication should be taken, (g) possible side effects of the medication, (h) the child's feelings and attitude about taking medication, and of course, (i) the parent's feelings about their son or daughter taking medication.

8. **I have heard that taking anti-depressant medications could increase the risk of my child having suicidal thoughts and therefore might increase the risk of suicide:**
   Unfortunately, there has been increased alarm about the possibility that taking anti-depressants can increase the risk of suicidal thoughts; however, there is insufficient evidence to support such a notion. While some people that take anti-

depressant medications have in fact committed suicide or made an attempt, this does not mean that the medication they were prescribed caused these thoughts or impulsive behaviors. One could utilize the same analogy about attending church, since some people who attend church have experienced suicidal thoughts or even completed suicide. Your doctor can explain that the medication is used to help re-establish the chemical balance within the body and really is not a "mind altering" drug.

9. **Treating children with medication leads to drug dependency:**
Research in drug addiction and dependency does not support the notion that children who are properly diagnosed and prescribed appropriate medications to help manage various symptoms such as impulsivity or angry outbursts later become addicts. What appears more predominant in clinical practice is the connection between children who were not treated with medication that could have been helpful and their subsequent drug usage and possible addiction. By the time the untreated child reaches middle school, his or her frustration is so high that it isn't unusual to find experimentation with alcohol, pot-smoking, or other drug usage "to feel better." Properly diagnosed and treated children don't seem nearly as likely to experiment with drugs during middle and high school years. Some experts actually believe that appropriately administered medication may help prevent children from developing more serious problems, and thus reduce the risk of such experimentation that is common among junior high or high school students.

10. **Food allergies may cause behavioral changes in my child:**
While some children appear more affected or show increased sensitivity to certain food products such as sugar, milk, nuts, chocolate, or preservatives and food dyes, scientific evidence does not give strong support for the role of food allergies or sensitivities causing various behavior problems. Obviously a reduction of sweets or foods containing excessive preservatives and dyes would be a good decision; however this should be done in the most inconspicuous way possible and not in a manner that could cause stigma to the child among his/her peers.

11. Medication will change my child's personality, will make him/her like a "zombie" or otherwise over emotional:

While in the past many children who were medicated for hyperactivity or attention problems were quite often over-medicated and therefore experienced several side effects such as these, recent changes in the manner in which doctors prescribe this medication has significantly lowered the risk of side effects. We have slowed down the whole prescribing process and start the child on the very smallest dose possible which generally causes no side effects. The doctor then slowly increases the medication (this process is called "titration") until the appropriate dosage is reached. Medication is used only to help the child better manage his behavior and reduce his/her propensity to over-react or have outbursts—not alter his thinking or emotional state. The medication will not alter his emotional state or change his personality; it will only help him/her be able to exhibit the true personality which will be more positive and rewarding than the behaviors that previously characterize outbursts. The child's self esteem is usually improved since he/she is getting far less negative feedback from the adults and finding peer relationships easier than before being on the medication.

12. Rather than use medication, using natural products such as herbs or natural foods and substances are safer:

Essentially, there is very little control over the herbal/natural food products in the USA. The FDA, a governmental agency that controls the production and usage of all medications, does not and will not obligate itself to also mange the herbal products. While there may be some products that could be helpful, we still do not know enough about these products and what they do within the body. The rigorous testing and standardization that FDA requires for all medications prior to approving them for the market is not done with the herbal/natural food product industry. We do not know how to dose them and what we do know about some of these products is still too limited to appropriately recommend their usage. Some parents claim that since these products are natural they are "safe." Most personnel working in such natural product stores have no formalized training and are recommending products that they claim are equivalent to medications prescribed by physicians who have had extensive medical training and practice. Many things come in natural forms that are toxic and can have extremely dangerous side effects especially when combined with other substances or medications. Arsenic comes in the natural form, but we know that it is poisonous and will cause death. Until further study and control of these products can be established, we discourage their usage.

13. **Taking medication will lower my child's self-esteem:**
Taking medication may actually do just the opposite; a child constantly getting into trouble for uncontrolled anger or other outbursts begins experiencing poor self-esteem. He/she begins to feel they can't control their emotions or feelings and very often gives up trying to gain better control. Once the child's behavior is more controlled with the help of medication, he/she will experience disciplinary interventions less, enjoy better peer relationships, and feel more normal or equal to peers rather than feeling "different" or "odd" as prior to gaining such control of their emotions.

14. **Medication will cause growth suppression in children:**
While some medications may cause a decrease in appetite, the pediatrician or physician prescribing the medication will monitor this possible side effect closely and make appropriate alterations in dosage, time of administration, or type of medication to minimize this risk.

15. **Leaning while under medication will not transfer when the child is no longer medicated:**
Learning is essentially more possible for the child who is properly medicated since his emotional responses are more within his/her control. He/she can give focus to what is being taught as opposed to worrying about what others think about his uncontrollable behavior and emotional outbursts.

Ask your doctor about any concerns or questions you might have regarding the use of medications and appropriate management of them. Knowledge is a powerful tool that helps reduce our concerns and clarifies misperceptions we may have because of things we have heard or read about.

STICKERS AND VISUAL AIDS TO REMIND THE CHILD TO STOP...THINK...AND THEN DO

Making stickers for notebooks, book bags, homework assignment sheets or other significant items that he/she will see several times a day can help provide a visual cue and will remind the child to follow the plan of STOP...THINK...DO! Most teachers will permit such stickers to be used within the classroom and at the student's desk. Stickers can be placed on little cards folded in half to allow them to stand up and serve as signs. Placement of such cards can be on desk at school, bed stand or dresser in bedroom, the counter where child brushes his/her teeth in the morning and evening, and even at child's place at the breakfast table or on the refrigerator where all the important messages for the family are posted. With all those reminders, the child should be able to remember to follow the new plan of STOP...THINK...before I DO!

Parents and teachers are also encouraged to use the same lingo with the child when cautioning him/her about a decision they have made or about to make by saying things like: "Did you stop and think before you made that decision?"..."I bet if you would have stopped and thought about it prior to making that choice, you might not be in trouble!"..."Please remember to Stop...Think...Do...in making your decision."

Children also like to design big posters like the traffic light or some of the other illustrations in the child's section of this book. This would be a great activity to do together; it makes for a fun and very constructive, learning experience.

If you could find a flashing light with red, yellow, and green lights—similar to a traffic light, this might provide the ultimate visual cue for the home or classroom setting.

Here are two examples of stickers that can be made at home:

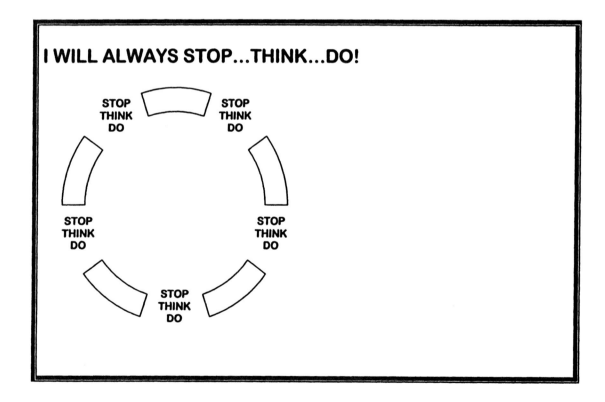

Here is an example of a poster you can help your child create as a visual reminder to utilize the STOP...THINK...DO program. Encourage them to color the various arrows with red, yellow, and green.

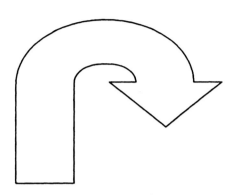

STOP...STOP...STOP...STOP!

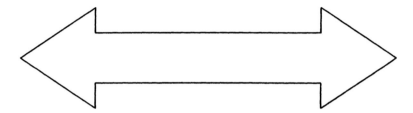

THINK...THINK...THINK...THINK!

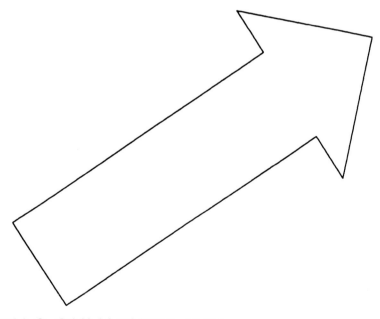

THEN & ONLY THEN, DO!

The traditional stoplight makes an excellent symbol for posters and stickers. If you can purchase such a lamp for your child's room, this would even further dramatize the importance of STOPPING to THINK before choosing to DO!

The following OBSERVATION CHECKLIST is a good way to objectively evaluate your child's behaviors. This checklist can be completed by parents and teachers; it may serve to provide a baseline and subsequent ratings used to compare and determine progress.

OBSERVATION CHECKLIST FOR PARENTS & TEACHERS

Name of Child: _____ Age: ____ Grade: ____

Date of Evaluation: _____ Person Completing Observation: _____

Please rate the child on the following items by placing an X or checkmark in the appropriate column:

Behaviors Observed	Not At All	Just A Little	Pretty Much	Very Much
AGG				
Has stolen from others				
Is cruel to animals				
Bullies peers or younger children				
Has been physically cruel to other people				
Initiates physical fights				
Has used a weapon that can cause serious harm				
Has forced someone into sexual activity				
Violates the rights of others				
Plays with toys recklessly, putting others at risk of injury				
Uses profanity around or towards others				
Attacks others—scratching, biting, kicking, etc.				
PD				
Has set fires				
Has destroyed property that belongs to others				
D & TH				
Has broken into someone else's property				
Lies to obtain favors or avoid responsibility				
Has stolen items without confronting victim				
SVR				
Stays out after curfew				
Runs away from home				
Is truant from school				
Please turn form over and complete items on backside **Thank you**				

114

ODD				
Loses temper				
Argues with adults				
Defies or refuses to comply with adult's requests or rules				
Deliberately annoys people				
Blames others for his/her mistakes				
Is touchy and easily annoyed by others				
Is angry and resentful				
Is spiteful or vindictive				
G				
Pouts and sulks				
Does not conform to limits on own without control from others				
Argues and must have last word in verbal exchanges				
Will not obey unless threatened with punishment				
Appears angry and generally having an uncooperative attitude or disposition				
Blames others for own mistakes or decisions				
Smiles rarely and has generally angry expression				

ADDITIONAL COMMENTS BY OBSERVER THAT WOULD BE HELPFUL:

Endnotes

American Psychiatric Association: Diagnostic and Statistical Manual of Mental Disorders, Fourth Edition, Text Revision. Washington DC, American Psychiatric Association, 2000.

Parent's Notations From Teachers, Counselors, and their Child's Doctor

ᵖSIA information can be obtained at www.ICGtesting.com
ᵖnted in the USA
ᵖOW06s0612280714

50529BV00002B/16/P